Socks and Secrets

readingbasics**plus**

HARPER & ROW, PUBLISHERS   New York   Philadelphia   Hagerstown   San Francisco   London

Standard Book Number 06-517107-1   1980 Printing   80818283RRD98765432

CONTRIBUTORS

DOLORES R. AMATO
A. DICKSON CARROLL
CHERIE A. CLODFELTER
LYNETTE SAINE GAINES
ERIC P. HAMP
PHILLIP L. HARRIS
JOSEPH A. LUCERO
EARL F. RANKIN
MATTIE CLAYBROOK WILLIAMS

Special acknowledgment to Sister Colette Zirbes and Marilyn Buckley Hanf.

ACKNOWLEDGMENTS

"The Bear's Toothache," an adaptation of *The Bear's Toothache* written and illustrated by David McPhail. Copyright © 1972 by David McPhail. By permission of Little, Brown and Company in association with The Atlantic Monthly Press, Boston.

"Come Here, Cat," an adaptation of *Come Here, Cat* by Joan L. Nødset. Text copyright © 1973 by Joan L. Nødset. Pictures copyright © 1973 by Steven Kellogg. Reprinted by permission of Harper & Row, Publishers, Inc., New York.

"De Koven," from *Bronzeville Boys and Girls* by Gwendolyn Brooks. Copyright © 1956 by Gwendolyn Brooks Blakely. Reprinted by permission of Harper & Row, Publishers, Inc., New York.

"Firefly," from *Under the Tree* by Elizabeth Madox Roberts. Copyright 1922 by B. W. Huebsch, Inc. Copyright 1930; renewed © 1958 by The Viking Press, Inc. Copyright 1950 by Ivor S. Roberts. Reprinted by permission of The Viking Press, Inc., New York.

"Georgie," adapted from *Georgie* by Robert Bright. Copyright 1944 by Doubleday & Company, Inc. Adapted with permission of Doubleday & Company, Inc., New York.

"In My Mother's House," adapted from *In My Mother's House* by Ann Nolan Clark. Copyright 1941; renewed © 1969 by Ann Nolan Clark. Reprinted by permission of The Viking Press, Inc., New York.

EDITORIAL Carol Goldman, Marguerite Liston, Eileen D. Schaubert, Elaine S. Goldberg, Diane K. Lindeman, Sylvia J. Rosenstein, Elise C. Leahy

EXECUTIVE EDITOR Martha A. Hayes

SENIOR EDITOR Eddy Jo Bradley

DESIGN Jane Ito, Mary Beth Bostrom, Lydia Halverson, Kristin Nelson

ILLUSTRATION

Ben Black pages 26-31; Lorinda Bryan Cauley pages 38-41, 108-113; Olivia Cole pages 32-37, 122; Kinuko Y. Craft pages 71-78; Peter Cross pages 107, 179; Diane DeGroat pages 17, 106; John Downs pages 91-96; Len Ebert pages 18-24; John Faulkner pages 79-84; Larry Frederick pages 162-169; Leigh Grant pages 170-171; Jean Helmer pages 156-161; Steven Kellogg pages 56-62; Arnold Lobel pages 84-90; Robert Masheris pages 7, 51, 97, 145; David McPhail pages 180-185; Heidi Palmer pages 65-69; Chris Santoro pages 136-144; William Shires pages 186-192; Krystyna Stasiak pages 16, 42; Arvis Stewart pages 115-121; Lynn Titleman page 179; Lorna Tomei pages 54, 55, 70; Kyuzo Tsugami pages 8-9, 52-53, 97-99, 146-147; Justin Wager pages 25, 44-45, 63, 114; John Wallner pages 10-15, 100-105; Terry Wickart pages 130-135; Jennie Williams pages 154, 155.

PHOTOGRAPHY

Dale Ahearn page 48 right; Bill Benoit page 46 left; The Bettmann Archive pages 173-174; B. Binzen/Image Bank cover and title page; Brown Brothers page 172; Tom England pages 123-129; Courtesy of Harper & Row, Publishers, Inc. page 120; Michal Heron pages 148-153; Jeroboam, Inc./Eileen Christelow pages 47 left, 49 top right, Kent Reno page 50 bottom left; Christopher B. Kuhn page 50 top center; Lockheed Aircraft Corporation pages 176-177; Photo Researchers/Ron Austing page 48 top, Karl Maslowski page 43 left; Leith Rohr pages 46 bottom right, 49 top left, 49 bottom left, 50 center; Courtesy of Seth Thomas, Inc. page 46 top right; Tom Stack and Associates, Inc./Bob Hamburgh page 47 bottom right, Ed and Dolores Kumler page 43 bottom right, Tom Myers page 48 left, Irene Stack page 50 top left; Ellis Herwig/Stock, Boston, Inc. page 50 bottom right; Time-Life Picture Agency, Arthur Rickerby page 29; United Press International page 28; Wide World Photos pages 26, 31, 175, 178; Zenith Radio Corporation page 47 top right.

Photographs on pages 148-153 were taken at Binney & Smith Company, Eaton, Pennsylvania.

CONTENTS

Collection 1

Collection 2

Collection 1

Words You Can Read

boy	bricks	ears
fire	money	pony
walls	water	wings

Words You Can Read

a	e	i	o	u
pass	yell	still	block	bugs
Jack	well	hill	clock	
	tell	wins	mop	
		chick	tossed	
		lit		

big + er   big + g + er = bigger

fire + fly = firefly

1. We like to walk <u>around</u> the block.
2. He knows how to do it by <u>himself</u>.
3. She does not live far away.
   She lives <u>near</u> us.

What Is It Now? by Tanner Janson

Steve was sitting on his front steps when Julie came out.

"What are you doing, Steve?" she asked.

"I came out to see if the rain had stopped," said Steve.
"I don't want to play in the house. What have you got, Julie?"

"Don't you know what this
is, Steve?" said Julie.
"I'll show you.
Look at what I'm doing with it.
I could be in a show.
I could be on TV, and everyone
could see me.
Now do you know what this is?"

"That is good, Julie," said Steve.
"But I can do something with it, too.
I can talk into it, and everyone
will hear me.
If I were in front of many
people, they could all hear what I say.
Can you hear me, Julie?"

"I can hear you, Steve," said Julie.
"And I can see you, too.
I can look into this and see
things that are very far away.
I can see things up in the sky.
Now I can see Ted!"

"Ted, help us with this," said Julie.
"We can move it and go over it."

"Or we can make something
to eat," said Ted.
"Let me show you."

Steve and Julie and Ted
did not see Sue
come up the steps.

14

"What are all of you doing?" said Sue.
"Don't you want to come and play?"

"Look what Sue has to play
 with," said Ted.
"I know what we all can do now."

"What?" said Sue.

"We will show you," they all said.

And they did.

When
by Marguerite Farrell

When you are older
And don't play in the cold,
Will you <u>still</u> know
How your hands feel in snow?

When you are older
And don't play in the rain,
Will you forget
How it feels to get wet?

When I Feel Like It

by Daniel Wetstone

When I feel like it,
I sit in green grass
And see the <u>bugs</u> <u>pass</u>.
I like it when they stop.

When I feel like it,
I run up on the <u>hill</u>
And keep <u>still</u>.
I like to feel on top.

Pam by Judith Davis

My name is Pam.
I have to be in a wheelchair.
I can't walk, and I can't climb
a tree.
But there are many things I can do.
I like to read, and I like to
work hard.

18

I can go to Kim's house
by myself.
She lives on my side of the street.
Sometimes we play inside her house,
and sometimes we play on the grass.
Sometimes Kim wheels my wheelchair,
but I can do it myself.

On a nice day we go up and down the street, from one end of the <u>block</u> to the other end.

Sometimes Kim runs far in front of me.

But she does not do it to be mean.

We are just playing.

I can run far in front of her, too!

Sometimes Kim <u>wins</u>. Sometimes I win.

Kim and I like to go swimming.
I know how to swim.
Sometimes the <u>water</u> feels so cold
that I <u>yell</u> when I first put my
feet in the water.
I don't mean to yell, but it
makes Kim laugh.
That makes me feel good inside.

One day in school Kim and I saw some pictures of children who live very far away.

We talked about what we saw in the pictures.

Some children were playing.

Some were on a <u>pony</u>.

Some were in a tree.

22

"Look at what the children are doing,"
said Kim.

"They like to do the same things we
do," I said.

"I like to ride a <u>pony</u>, too,"
said Kim.

"And I like to play," I said.

"People can live very far away, but
they can like the same things."

Sometimes I think about what I
will be when I am <u>bigger</u>.
Kim and I talk about it, too.
There are so many things I can be!
There are so many things I can do!

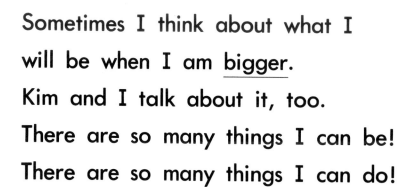

myself

Can You Find Them?

If this boy looks <u>around</u>, he can
find many things.

Can you see a <u>bug</u>, a <u>clock</u>,
a <u>mop</u>, a <u>chick</u>, and a frog?

What other things can you find?

Lee Trevino   by Gillian Williams

Do you know how to play golf?
Lee Trevino does.
You can see him
playing golf here.

When Lee Trevino was a boy,
he learned to play golf
all by himself.
At night he would play golf
on the grass near his house.

When he was older,
he played golf all the time.
Now he plays golf very <u>well</u>.
He <u>wins</u> many prizes.

Lee Trevino likes to have fun
when he plays in golf games.
He likes to laugh, and he likes
to make other people laugh.

One time it started to rain when
he was playing in a golf game.
He did not run inside.
But he did not get wet!

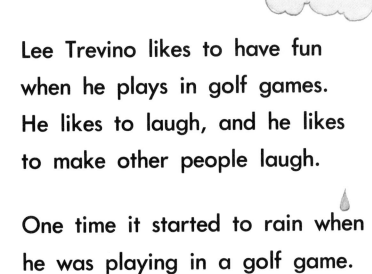

Sometimes Lee Trevino plays golf
with his friend, Jack.
At the start of one game they played,
Lee Trevino had a surprise.
He pulled out a play snake and
tossed it to his friend, Jack.
At first, Jack backed away from
the snake, and then he laughed.
All the people around them laughed, too.

Lee Trevino likes to help people.
When he wins at golf, he gives some of
his prize money away.

Sometimes Lee Trevino has a party for
the children who come to see him play golf.
He gives them hamburgers, ice cream, and
other good things to eat.

33

34

36

37

In My Mother's House

by Ann Nolan Clark

This is my mother's house.

My father and mother made it.

They made it with adobe bricks.

They made it big.

They made it high.

This is my mother's house.

I live in it.

In my mother's house there is
a fireplace.
On dark nights the fire is bright.

39

On cold nights the <u>fire</u> is warm.
The fire is there to help me see
and to keep me warm.

In my mother's house all day I play
and work.
All night I sleep.

40

The <u>walls</u> come around
me in a good way.
I can see them.
I can feel them.
I live with them.

This house is good to me.
It keeps me.
I like it.
This is my mother's house.

Firefly

by Elizabeth Madox Roberts

A little light is going by,
Is going up to see the sky,
A little light with wings.

I never could have thought of it,
To have a little bug all lit
And made to go on wings.

Sounds Around You

by Paul Duci

Sounds are all around you.
Think about all the sounds
you can hear.
Are there very many?

There are high sounds,
little sounds, and big sounds.
There are many different sounds
made by many different things.

You know that you hear with your ears.
But do you know how you hear?
When you hear your father call
you, the sound has to go from where
he is to your ears.

The sound will go first to the inside
of your <u>ears</u>.
This is what the inside of an ear looks like.

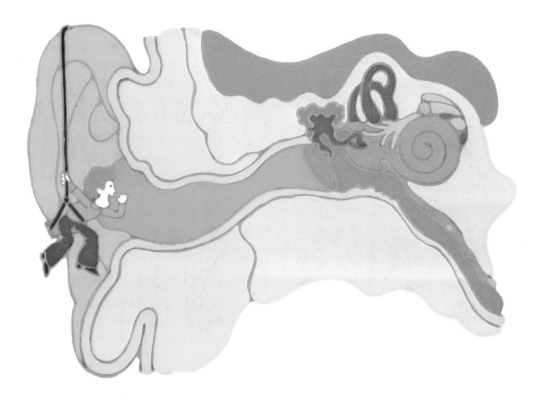

All the things in your ear work to
help you hear.
Sounds move very, very fast.
You can hear your father at the very same
time he starts to talk.

What you hear can change how you feel
and what you do.
You can hear something that makes
you feel happy and laugh.
But there are some sounds you don't
like to hear.
Can you think of some sounds that make
you feel sad?

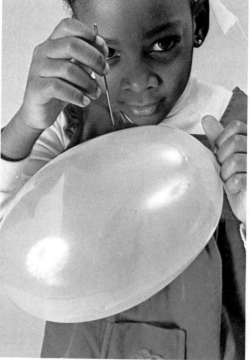

You can hear something that makes you
feel like going to sleep.
Do some sounds keep you from sleeping?

Sounds can <u>tell</u> you things you
have to know.
Sounds can tell you if you
can play outside or have to play inside.

A sound can make you feel afraid.
Or a sound can make you feel safe.
Can you think of a sound that makes
you feel safe?
What is it?
Can you think of a sound that
makes you afraid?
What is it?
Sometimes when it is dark, a little
noise sounds like a big noise!

Sounds can make you think of
eating something.
What foods make a noise when you eat
them?

Sometimes you don't know what it is
you are hearing!
It is fun to put something over your
eyes and listen to the sounds around you.
Do this now.
Can you name all the sounds you hear?

Collection 2

Words You Can Read

barn

dog

door

face

owl

tail

cry + ed = cryed = cried

live + ed = liveed = lived

surprise + ed = surpriseed = surprised

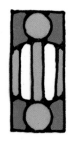

I would	did not
I woul d	did n o t
I'd	didn't

Words You Can Read

a	e	i	o
flat	pet	lick	knocked

bed + room = bedroom

1. The <u>wind</u> will blow my hat away.
2. I <u>hurt</u> my hand when I played with my cat.
3. Look for the green light <u>before</u> you walk across the street.
4. You can go outside <u>after</u> you put the game away.

Wind

by Fritz Nelson

Blowing in the night,
Blowing in the day.
Wind, Wind,
Blowing all around us.

I'd like to know.
I'd like to know.
When you stop, Wind,
Where do you go?

Rain

by S. Nishimura

A
chain
of
rain
comes
down
from
the
sky
and
lands
on
me.

Come Here, Cat

by Joan L. Nødset

Come here, cat.

Come here, you good cat.

I like you, cat.

Why don't you come?

Don't you like me?

Then I'll come to you, cat.

Can I <u>pet</u> you, cat?

56

I did not mean to pull your tail.
You ran away when I was petting it.
Did I hurt you, cat?
I hurt your feelings.
I did not mean to.

I'll put you on my lap.
Stay here now.
That is a good cat.
You can lick my face.
That feels good.
I like you, too, cat.

Don't bite me, cat!
Don't! Don't! Don't!
Bad cat!

Were you playing?
You scared me, cat.
But it is OK now.
You can come back, cat.

Did I scare you, too?
Look, I'll sit here.
You will be safe here.
Please, please come back!

I like you, cat.
Oh, cat!
I hear your motor.

What Is the Word?

The cat ran away when I _____ it.

You can not _____ the squirrel.

    pet   petted

The new little puppy started to _____.

The kitty _____ all night.

    cry   cried

Bill _____ his socks.

How can I _____ the sound of the motor?

    change   changed

"Are your feet dry?" _____ Father.

We will _____ Grandmother.

    ask   asked

Did you see a spark _____ out of the fire?

We went one way, and we _____ back another way.

      come   came

Jack _____ to the party, but he could not stay.

The little boy did not want to _____ with us.

      go   went

The puppy _____ a noise, but it was not hurt.

A firefly's wings _____ it go very fast.

      make   made

Food for the Animals

by Gail M. Allosso

When it's very cold, it's hard for
some animals to find things to eat.
You can help them.
You can put food out for them.
Start putting the food outside before
it gets too cold.
Keep putting it out every night.
Don't change where you put the food.
That way the animals will learn where
to go to find food.
They are smart.
They will come back again and again.

You can make something just for
birds to eat.
You have to have one cup of peanut
butter and two cups of dry oatmeal.
Put the peanut butter into a pot.
Then put in the oatmeal.
The birds will like the peanut butter
and oatmeal.
It is good for them.

Dip pine cones into the pot of peanut butter and oatmeal.

Put the pine cones all over a tree.

You can put bits of dry bread and some berries on the same tree.

You can put nuts and dry oatmeal on the snow around the tree.

Many different birds will come to eat.

You can do something to help bigger
animals find food, too.
Put peanut butter all over the top of
something <u>flat</u> and hard.
Then put it outside at night.
You may not see the animals when
they come to eat the peanut butter.
But in the morning when it is light,
look for tracks they made.

Animal tracks in the peanut butter or
on the snow around it can tell you what
animals live near you.
Every animal makes different tracks.

Use the pictures to find out what
animals come to eat your food.
You may find out there are some animals
that live near you that you never see.

A Little Dog

by Lois Lenski

A little dog
not big at all,
A little dog
to come when we call.
A dog to bark
and jump and play,
A dog to run
with us all day!

Georgie

by Robert Bright

Mr. and Mrs. Whittaker lived in a little house.

In this little house there was a little ghost.

His name was Georgie.

Every night Georgie would give the steps a little creak.

Then he would give the door a little squeak.

And that was how Mr.
and Mrs. Whittaker knew it was
time to go to bed.
And Herman, the cat, knew it was
time to go out.

And Miss Oliver, the <u>owl</u>, knew it was
time to get up and say "Whoooo!"

And so it went.

Then Mr. Whittaker got it into his head to
fix the steps and to fix the <u>door</u>.
Now Georgie could not make the steps
creak and could not make the door squeak.

SQUEAK

So Mr. and Mrs. Whittaker didn't know
when it was time to go to bed.
And Herman didn't know when it was
time to go out.
And Miss Oliver didn't know when it was
time to get up, and she went on sleeping.
And Georgie sat by himself and looked
very sad.

Georgie went out to find a different house to live in.

He ran to this house and to that house.

Every house had a ghost.

After looking at many houses, Georgie ran away to a barn.

A lot of time went by, and it
rained and it snowed.
And out in a corner of the barn,
Georgie was not happy at all.
He was cold from the wind that was
blowing around the barn walls.
He was wet from the rain and
snow that came in the barn door.

But the rain and snow did something
to the steps and the door of the
Whittaker house.

It was Herman who first learned about it.
And he told Miss Oliver.
Miss Oliver went to find Georgie.
She told him that now the steps would
creak and the door would squeak again.
What good news that was for Georgie!
He jumped up and ran right back to
the house.

So once again, at the same old time, the steps creaked and the door squeaked.

And Mr. and Mrs. Whittaker knew when it was time to go to sleep again.

And Herman knew when it was time to go out again.

And Miss Oliver knew when it was time to get up again and say "Whoooo!"

Riddles

1. What is the first thing you put on every day?

2. How do you find a squirrel?

3. What do you call hard water?

4. What does everyone get at the same time?

1. You put your feet on the ground.

2. You sit in a tree and act like a nut.

3. You call it ice.

4. Everyone gets older.

Riddles, Riddles

1. Why do you have ears on the sides of your head?

2. Why do you go to bed every night?

3. What is a cat after it is two years old?

1. So your hat will not come down over your eyes.

2. Because the bed will not come to you.

3. It is three years old.

1. A man and his brother fell into the water.
   The man got his hair wet, but his brother did not. Why not?

2. What did one street say to another street?

3. What do you do when something scares you?

3. Ice cream!

2. "I'll see you at the corner."

1. Because his brother didn't have any hair!

It's a Dog's World

by Roy Bradley

I'm talking to you.
Can't you tell what
I'm saying?

Run fast! Slow down!
I wish they knew what
they wanted.

It's my bark.
If you don't like it, don't
listen.

Didn't you see me scare that big dog?

He told me my <u>tail</u> had to be fixed.

Everyone around here grows and grows. Why can't I?

Just because I'm a dog, they think I don't have any feelings.

83

Upstairs
and Downstairs

by Arnold Lobel

Owl's house had an upstairs and
a downstairs.
Some of the time Owl was
upstairs in his bedroom.
At other times Owl was
downstairs in his living room.

When Owl was downstairs, he said,
"I wonder how my upstairs is?"

When Owl was upstairs, he said,
"I wonder how my downstairs is?
I am always missing one or the other."

"Maybe if I run very, very fast,
I can be upstairs and downstairs
at the same time."

Owl ran up the stairs.
"I am up," he said.

Owl ran down the stairs.
"I am down," he said.

Owl ran up and down the stairs
faster and faster.

"Owl!" he cried.
"Are you downstairs?"

There was no answer.

"No," said Owl.
"I am not downstairs because
I am upstairs.
I am not running as fast
as I should."

"Owl!" he shouted.
"Are you upstairs?"

There was no answer.

"No," said Owl.
"I am not upstairs
because I am downstairs.
I'd better run faster."

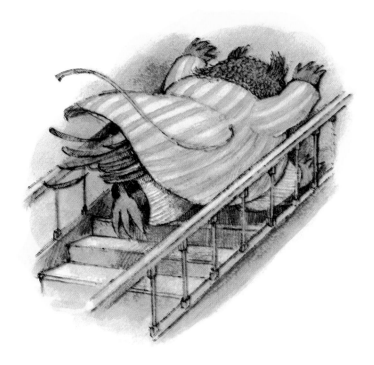

"Faster, faster, faster!" cried Owl.

Owl ran upstairs and downstairs
all night.
But he could not be upstairs
and downstairs at the same time.

"When I am up, I am not down,"
said Owl.
"When I am down, I am not up.
All I am is very tired!"

And so Owl sat down.

And he sat on the step that was
right in the middle.

The Surprise   by Gerry Jung

Liwayway Santa Cruz was looking at
a page in her book.
But she was not really reading.
She was thinking of all the fun she
was going to have in the next two
days.
The start of the fiesta would be
that night.
The fiesta was a happy time.
It made Liwayway think of the
Philippines.

The fiesta was two days of fun from
morning to night.
Liwayway and her brother, Renaldo,
thought the fiesta was the best
time of year.

There was always lots of good food
to eat at the fiesta.
Liwayway and Renaldo helped make
all kinds of food.
Liwayway's face lit up just
thinking about the good
things to eat.

Just then Liwayway's mother and
Renaldo walked into the room.

"I want to talk to you, children," Mrs.
Santa Cruz said.
"You two know that your father feels
sad at this time of year.
At fiesta time he thinks about his
own mother far off in the Philippines.
And this makes him sad.
Well, I have a surprise for him.
Lola Maria is flying here right now.
Your grandmother will be here tonight."

Liwayway and Renaldo jumped
up and down.

"Oh, good!" cried Liwayway
and Renaldo.

"Shhhh," said Mrs. Santa Cruz.
"I don't want your father to know
about it until Lola Maria gets here.
It's a surprise!"

"Renaldo and I will not say a word,"
said Liwayway.

It was a long day for Liwayway
and Renaldo.
When it was dark outside, they both
started to look out at the street.
Then they both listened for sounds
at the door.

"We have to stop looking and listening
like this," said Liwayway.
"Father may want to know what we
are doing."

Just then someone knocked at
the door.

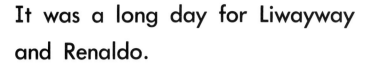

95

Liwayway's father went to the door.
There was Lola Maria.

Mr. Santa Cruz was so surprised that
all he could say was "Oh!"

Everyone laughed and talked as
Lola Maria came into the room.

"Now it is really fiesta!" said
Liwayway.

Collection 3

Words You Can Read

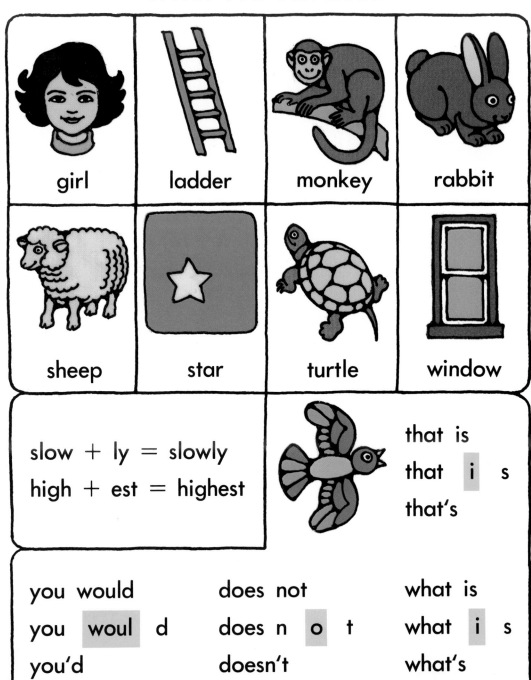

girl	ladder	monkey	rabbit
sheep	star	turtle	window

slow + ly = slowly
high + est = highest

that is
that i s
that's

you would   does not   what is
you woul d   does n o t   what i s
you'd   doesn't   what's

Words You Can Read

	a	e	i	o
	bags	yet	kids	spot
		smell		shops

ā
shake
take

ī
white
shine
bike

1. <u>Wash</u> your hands before eating.
2. Can you <u>write</u> your name?
3. The <u>fence</u> went all around the house.
4. She put her hand inside her <u>pocket</u>.
5. I know you can do it if you <u>try</u>!

How to Grow Sprouts   by Steve Workman

Everyone can find room to grow sprouts.

Sprouts grow from some kinds of beans.

The little beans get bigger and bigger.

Then sprouts pop out.

The sprouts are very good for you.

You will like them.

If you want to, you can eat sprouts with other foods.

Here is what you have to do to
grow sprouts.
First, get some beans.
If you can, get some mung beans.
If you can't get mung beans, you
can get another kind of beans
that will sprout.
Next, get a big jar, a
cloth to put over the jar, and
some water.

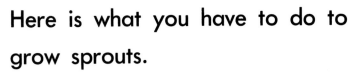

Then put some beans into your jar.
Cover the beans with water.
Let the jar of beans and water sit
where it is warm and dark all night.
In the morning the beans will be a
little bigger.
Cover the top of the jar with the cloth.
Let the water run out very slowly.
Don't shake the jar.

Now <u>wash</u> the beans in the jar by
letting water run in and out.
Keep the jar covered with the cloth
when you wash the beans.
Then turn the jar on its side and <u>take</u>
it back to the warm <u>spot</u>.
Wash the beans once every morning and
once every night in this way.

The sprouts grow fast.

After one day they will start to grow.

After three or four days they will be

big enough to eat.

Eat them when they are

this long.

If you don't eat all the sprouts

right away, keep them cold.

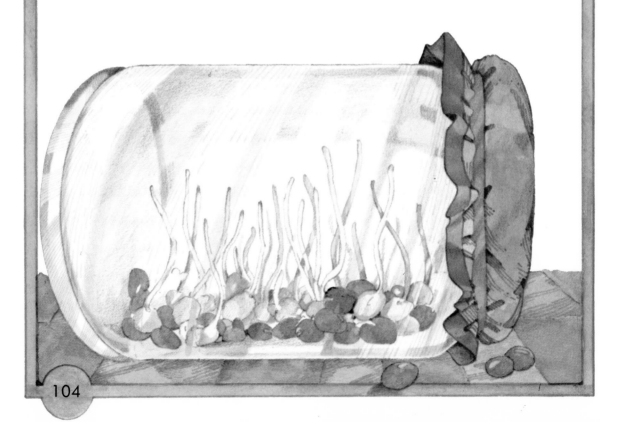

Here are some things you can make with
your sprouts.
Can you think of more ways to use the
sprouts you grow?

If by Bobbi Katz

If I were a giant,
  I'd reach so high
Until I felt the fur clouds
  That ride in the sky.
If I were a giant,
  That's what I'd do.
I'd reach a white fur cloud
  And give it to you!

Listen! by Robert Frank

Did a noise reach your ears?
Listen! Bark, bark, bark!
That's the way my dog sounds
Before it gets fed.

Did a noise reach your ears?
Listen! Tick, tick, tick!
That's the way my clock sounds
When I get into bed.

Did a noise reach your ears?
Listen!
That's the way a thought sounds
As it grows inside your head.

The Mean Dragon

by Janice May Udry

Once there was a mean dragon who
always hid by rocks and walls.
Then he would jump out with
a terrible BOO!
This scared the socks off
everyone.
The dragon would laugh and laugh.

"Enough is enough," said a little <u>girl</u>.

And she went out to get some paper <u>bags</u>.
When she had enough bags, she got some
children to help her.
They stayed up nearly all night putting
terrible, mean faces on the paper bags.

They gave a paper <u>bag</u> to everyone.
Then they all walked up the hill to
the cave where the dragon went to
sleep at night.
They hid by a big rock.

In the morning the dragon came out
of his cave.

"BOO!"

The terrible, mean bag
faces jumped out at the dragon.

"URKK!" he yelled.

It scared his socks right off.
He did not stop to pick them up.
He ran down the hill and to the
next town.

Everyone laughed and laughed.
Then they put the dragon's socks on
a flagpole.
They flew them high over the town.

Find the Right Word

You can see them when it snows.

You can make it fly up high.

You can put it around a picture.

You can play on it until it's dark outside.

You can see it in front of some homes.

You can use them on the ice.

You can see its nice soft fur.

slide

frame

kite

gate

skates

fox

flakes

The City Girl by Polly Reardon

Once a little <u>girl</u> lived in the
big city of Chicago.
She did not talk a lot.
She liked to look at things and
think about them.
In her eyes every house and tree
was beautiful.
Her name was Gwendolyn Brooks.

There were not many trees in the city.
There was just a little green grass in
the parks.
But there were streets and cars and
many houses, and many people.
Gwendolyn liked to hear the people
talk and see the children play.

She had many beautiful thoughts
about city streets,
city houses, and city people.
Gwendolyn liked them all, and she
wrote her thoughts down on paper.
She made pictures with her words.
Word pictures like the ones Gwendolyn
wrote are called poems.

When Gwendolyn was very young, a newsman put one of her poems on a page in his newspaper.

He said, "One day everyone will hear more from this little girl.
She will do big things for people."

Gwendolyn worked hard when she
was at school.

She learned everything she could.

Her mother and father helped her.

When she walked down her own
street, she saw some good things and
some bad things.

In her poems she wrote about the
things she saw and felt.

Now Gwendolyn Brooks is older, and
she still puts her feelings into words.
She is always finding new ways to
write about her own city and
its people.
Many people read her poems and think
they are very beautiful.
Again and again Gwendolyn Brooks
has won prizes for her poems.

Gwendolyn Brooks <u>writes</u>
poems for everyone.
When we read her poems, we learn how
to look at things in a new
and different way.
We learn to think about things in
a way we never did before.
The things Gwendolyn says in her
poems help us see the world as
she sees it.

De Koven by Gwendolyn Brooks

You are a dancy little thing,
You are a rascal, <u>star</u>!
You seem to be so near to me,
And <u>yet</u> you are so far.

If I could get you in my hands
<u>You'd</u> never get away.
I'd keep you with me always.
You'd <u>shine</u> both night and day.

From My <u>Window</u>

by A. R. Moreno

This is my window.

I can look down from my

window and see many things.

I can see <u>shops</u> and houses

and cars and people.

I can see street lights and

treetops.

I can see nice things, like the ice cream truck.

123

From my window I can see the bodega,
where my mother and father always
shop for food.
Sometimes I help them do the shopping.
Shopping in the bodega is fun!
I like to smell all the good smells.
My sister works in the bodega after
school and on Saturdays.
She is working hard so she can get
enough money for her own bike.

I can see the play lot on my street, too.
Everyone on my street likes the
play lot very much.

Before, we had to play ball in
the street.
Now we play all kinds of games in
the play lot.
It is much better for us to play in
the play lot.

From my window I can see the house on the corner, where my friend Roberto lives. Sometimes we play on the steps in front of his house.
Sometimes we both just stay on the steps and look at the bigger kids playing baseball.

The bigger <u>kids</u> say that Roberto and
I are not big enough to play baseball
with them.
I know that's wrong because we play
baseball with my big sister and
her friends.
That's always fun.

In the morning I can look out my
window and see all the children
going to school.
Then I know it's time for me to go, too.
At night I can see my father coming
home from work.
He stops to get a newspaper before
he comes in.
When I see my father, I know it is
time to get ready to eat.
My mother does not go to work until
after we eat.
We are all asleep when she comes home.

I can see the snow and the rain from
my window.
At night I can see the bright stars from
my window.
What can you see from your window?

The Smart Monkey

by James Lum

A cat ran up a tree.
When the cat got to the top, it
looked down.

"I'm up much too high," said the cat.
"How can I get down?"

A duck came by.

"I can't get down," said the cat.
"What can I do?"

"Maybe I can help you,"
said the duck.
"Jump onto my back."

But the cat was afraid to
jump so far.

130

A rabbit came by.

"I can't get down," said the cat.
"Can you help me?"

"Yes, I'll help you," said the rabbit.
"I'll get on the duck, and you jump
onto my back.
My fur is soft so you will not
get hurt."

131

The rabbit got on the duck.

But the cat was not ready to jump that far.

Then along came a turtle.

"Can you help me get down?" asked the cat.

"Yes, I can help you," said the turtle. "I'll get on the duck and the rabbit, and you jump onto my back."

The turtle got on the rabbit and the rabbit got on the duck.

But the cat was still not ready to jump so far.

Next a sheep came along.

"What will happen to me?"
asked the cat.
"No one can help me get down."

"Maybe I can help," said the sheep.
"I'll get on the duck and the rabbit
and the turtle.
Then you just jump onto my back."

The sheep got on the turtle, the turtle
got on the rabbit, and the rabbit
got on the duck.

But the cat still was afraid to
jump so far.

Now along came a <u>monkey</u>
with a long tail.
It looked at all the animals.

"You look funny.
What are you doing?" the monkey
asked the animals.

"We are helping the cat," said the duck.

"It can't get down," said
the rabbit.

"The cat <u>doesn't</u> want to jump onto
my back," said the <u>sheep</u>.

"Because it's afraid,"
said the turtle.

"I know what to do," said the monkey.

It ran up the tree.
Then the quick monkey ran down the
tree with the cat on its back.

"Sometimes," said the monkey, "you
animals are not as smart as you think!
Good-by."

And off it ran.

Charlie's Jump

by Veronica Petrovich

Charlie Street reached out and
put one hand on the fence.
He put his other hand in his pocket.
He jumped as high as he could.
Up and over the fence he went.
Charlie Street felt good.

"Fences are for jumping," Charlie
thought as he came down on
the other side.

Then Charlie started to look for
something to do.
He was walking along with both hands in
his pockets when he saw his friend Ted.

"Charlie, what are you doing?" called
Ted.
"Any of our friends around?"

"Not that I know of," said Charlie.
"Margie is at the show with her brother.
Fred went fishing with his dad.
He will be back tonight."

"What can we do?" asked Ted.

"Well, we can go over to Ollie's house,"
  said Charlie.
"His house has high fences all around it.
  We all can jump the fences.
  Then we can see who can jump the
  highest fence."

"Oh, you are a whiz at jumping," said Ted.
"You always win when we jump.
  You can win with one hand in your pocket!
  It's no fun for me."

Charlie knew that was true.

But Ted could not think of anything, so the two boys went to Ollie's house.

"Ollie, come on out," they both called.

"We want to jump fences," called Charlie.

Ollie came out his front door and down the steps.
He sat down on the bottom step.
Ollie's face did not look happy.

"What's wrong?" asked Ted.

"Jump, jump, jump!" shouted Ollie.
"That's all Charlie wants to do!"

Ted looked down at the ground.
Charlie looked right at Ollie.

"You are mad because I can jump better
than you can jump," said Charlie.

"That's not true!" shouted Ollie.
"You are not that good.
 I know a fence in town you can't jump over.
 It's the big fence in front of the park."

"That fence is not so big," said Charlie.
"I can jump it."

"We will see about that!" said Ollie.
"You be at the park in the morning."

"I'll be there!" said Charlie.

141

Ted and Charlie started to walk home.

"Charlie, don't <u>try</u> that jump,"
said Ted.
"You will never make it.
That's the <u>highest</u> fence in town."

"Well, I can try.
I'm not going to just give up," said
Charlie.

He started to think about the fence in
front of the park.

The next morning Charlie and
Ted met Ollie.
Charlie had a ladder with him.
He put the ladder up to the fence, and
he climbed to the top of the ladder.
Next, he put one hand on the fence.
Then he jumped off the ladder over the top
of the fence.

It was a long way down.
He landed on his feet, and then he fell over.
From the ground he looked up at the sky.

"I made it!" Charlie thought.

143

"Oh, come on," shouted Ollie.
"Are you <u>trying</u> to be funny?
You didn't jump over the fence!"

"Yes, I did," yelled Charlie.
"You didn't say that I had to jump
from the ground.
You just said I had to jump over
the fence.
And I did!"

Collection 4

Words You Can Read

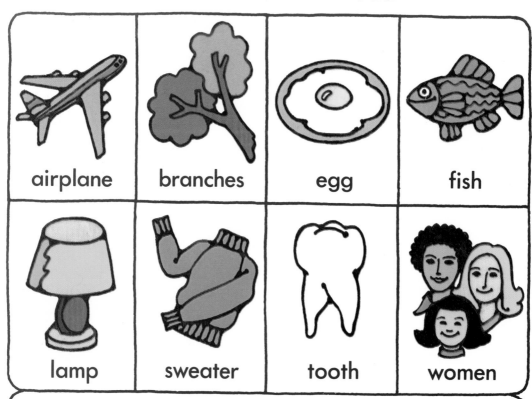

airplane	branches	egg	fish
lamp	sweater	tooth	women

is not   quick + est = quickest

is n o t

isn't

box + es = boxes

slide + ing = slideing = sliding

story + es = storyes = stories

Words You Can Read

a	e	i	o
wax	checked	drips	dots
packed	press	Cliff	job
last	West	trip	shocked
		sill	

ā	ī	ō
shape	lines	Stone
Lane	wide	woke
Space		rope
ate		

1. The sky is a beautiful blue.
2. She opened the window.
3. Reading is more fun than anything else.
4. I heard you call my name.
5. Look for the ball under the bed.
6. I had some cake. Now it's gone.

Crayons Are a Bright Idea!

by Rochelle Carroll

Do you have any idea how crayons are made?

First, a dry color is mixed with hot, wet <u>wax</u> in a vat.

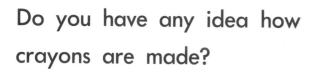

When the color and <u>wax</u> are well mixed,
the wax is spilled onto a table.
This table has round holes in it.
The holes are the <u>shape</u> of crayons.
The hot, colored wax <u>drips</u> into
the holes and fills them to the top.

After the wax in the holes gets hard,
some of it has to be scraped off.
Then up pop crayons!
If a crayon isn't just right, it is
pulled out.

The next step in making crayons
is to wrap them in paper.

Red crayons are wrapped in red paper.
Blue crayons are wrapped in blue paper.
All of the wrapped crayons of
the same color are checked and
put in a big box made of wood.

Then crayons of different colors
are ready to be <u>packed</u> into the
<u>boxes</u> you will see in
shops and at school.

Here the crayons are sliding quickly
into opened boxes.
Many boxes are packed at one time.

Then trucks take crates packed with
boxes of crayons to shops where
they are sold.
That is how crayons get from where
they are made to your house or school.

Are You Ready to Use Your Crayons?

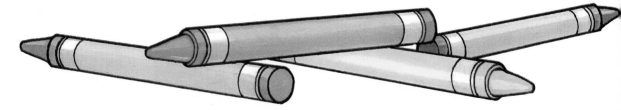

You know that you can make different kinds of <u>lines</u> with your crayons. If you <u>press</u> down hard with your crayons, you can make thick lines. If you press lightly, you can make thin lines on your paper. With the tip or the end of your crayons you can make <u>dots</u>, too.

Here is an idea for you to try.

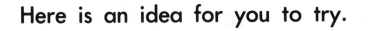

1. First, put many different colors on your paper. <u>Press</u> hard.

2. Then put another paper on top of the first one.

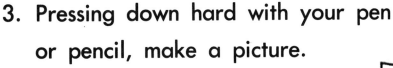

3. Pressing down hard with your pen or pencil, make a picture.

4. Now turn the picture over. What has happened?

155

The Egg and the Chick

by Sherre B. Levene

Look at an egg.

Do you know where an egg comes from?

It comes from a hen.

A hen makes an egg.

Do you know where a chick comes from?

It comes from an egg that a
mother hen makes.

A chick grows inside an egg for
three weeks.

An egg has to stay warm all the time
that a chick is growing inside it.
Sometimes a mother hen will sit
on her egg and keep it warm.
Sometimes an egg is put into
a warm box that looks like the one
you see here.

A chick gets all its food from the egg yolk.

After two weeks the chick starts to grow an egg <u>tooth</u>.

The egg tooth will help the chick crack the shell when it is time to come out.

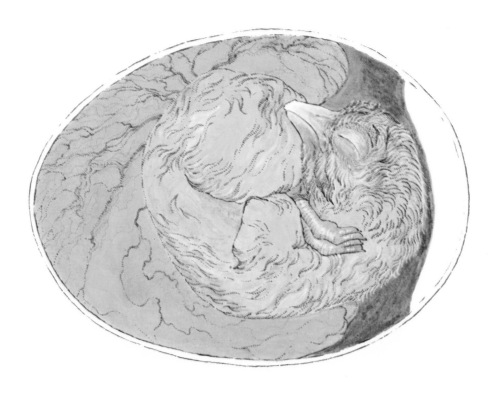

After three weeks the chick is big
enough to come out of its shell.
It hits the inside of the shell again
and again with its hard egg tooth.
This is very hard work for the
chick to do.
But the chick is ready to come out.
It hits the shell again and again and
then the thin shell starts to crack.

The chick cracks the thin shell all around.
Now the chick can get out
of the shell.

The new chick looks funny because it
is all wet.
It cannot get up by itself.

Before too long the chick is dry.
It looks like a soft ball of fuzz.
The chick can get up on its feet, and
it can eat some food.
By the next day it can walk by
itself and find food.
It will eat, and it will grow and
grow and grow.

In Africa   by C. L. Beaudry

Cindy Lane thought it was lots of
fun when she and her mother and father
moved to Africa.
Mr. and Mrs. Lane were taking
pictures of the animals in Africa.
Before she left her old home, Cindy gave
her pet snake to her friend Jo.
She gave her job as newsgirl to
her friend Pat.

Cindy knew she would find new and
different things to do in Africa.

One morning Cindy went into the woods in back of her new home. She started to climb a big tree in the woods.

"This is a nice high tree," Cindy said to herself.
"I'll see far, far away when I get to the top."

Cindy was still climbing up when she stopped to listen.
She could hear someone calling.

Cindy looked down, but she could not
see anything because the tree <u>branches</u>
were so thick.

"Where are you, Momo?" shouted someone.
"Are you up in that tree?"

Cindy came down far enough to
see a girl looking up at the tree.

"Who is Momo?" called Cindy.

The girl on the ground laughed.

"Momo is my pet monkey," said the girl.
"I thought he came to the woods here,
but now I can't find him."

"You have a monkey for a pet?" cried
Cindy.
"I'll help you find him.
Maybe he is here in the woods."

The girl's name was Rona.
She and Cindy started looking for Momo.
They saw the little monkey jumping from
branch to branch high in the trees.
He was too quick for them to catch in
the trees, but then he came down on
the ground and started running.

"Quick! Catch him!" yelled Rona.

Cindy reached for Momo's tail, but he
jumped away from her.
The little monkey ran around a corner.

"We will never catch him there in the
market," said Rona.

Cindy looked at the market.
There were many, many people and
many things to look at.
She saw men who had all kinds of
food to sell.
She saw women selling beautiful cloth.
But she didn't see a little monkey.

Cindy saw a big stack of bananas that
looked very good to eat.
But just then all the bananas fell to
the ground.
Out of the pile of bananas popped Momo!
Cindy and Rona started to run after the
monkey again.
But someone <u>else</u> reached out and
stopped him.

167

It was one of the <u>women</u> who sold cloth.

"That's my mother," said Rona.

Both girls and Momo felt tired from running,
so they sat down near Rona's mother.
She was selling a beautiful cloth of
bright red and blue and green.

"I have sold all my cloth," she said.
"If I had time to make more cloth,
I could have sold more."

"I have an idea," said Cindy.

She talked to Rona and Rona's
mother about her idea.
The next market day, Cindy and Rona
were at the market again.
But this time the girls were
selling cloth.

"My mother is really happy about our
idea," said Rona.
"And Momo is happy, too!"

Long Lane

Web Street

Cliff Street

Green
Woods

Red Pony Po

Stone Street

Reading a Map

A map is something that shows you
where things are.
If you can read a map, you can find
your way around a city or a town.
You can use a map to find
streets, parks, and mountains.
The map you see at the
top is a map of <u>West</u> Town.
What are the names of the streets?

170

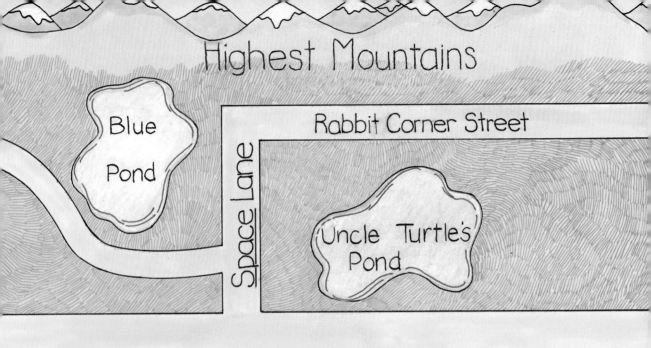

What do you think the three <u>blue</u>
pictures on this map mean?
They show the ponds in <u>West</u> Town.
What are the names of the ponds?
Look for lots of trees.
This is Green Woods.
What do you think would be the
<u>quickest</u> way to get from Green Woods
to Uncle Turtle's Pond? Why?
What is another way you could go?

by Gerry Jung

What Happened to AE?

"I will so fly an airplane," said Amelia.
"A girl can do anything she wants to do.
I want to fly an airplane more than
anything else."

When Amelia Earhart was young, many
people were afraid of airplanes.
But Amelia liked airplanes.
She thought flying would be fun.

Amelia went to flying school.
She learned all about airplanes and
how to fly them.
When she first started to learn,
she could not fly by herself.
But she did not stop trying.
She flew day after day until she
could fly an airplane by herself.

On one <u>trip</u> her airplane
ran out of gas.
Amelia knew she had to land and
get more gas.
She looked down and saw a <u>wide</u> street.
No cars or people were on the
street, and so she landed there.
The people who saw her airplane land
were <u>shocked</u> at first.
But they were happy to see Amelia.

Amelia Earhart was the first woman to
fly across the Atlantic Ocean.
She flew from the United States
to Ireland.
Newspaper stories about her reached
men and women all over the world.
People learned all about her and
called her AE.
Amelia went to the White House to
meet the President.

Amelia helped other people learn to fly.
But what she liked best to do was
fly to different lands.
She wanted to fly around the world.
People said she could not do it.

"I will be the first woman to do it,"
    said Amelia.

So Amelia left on her <u>trip</u> around the
world.
She would fly far, far away.

"Maybe she can do it after all,"
    people said.

But this would be Amelia's <u>last</u> trip.

Amelia flew her airplane into the dark sky.

She never came back home.

What happened to her?

Did she run out of gas again?

No one knows.

People tried to find her airplane, but could not find it.

And to this day, people wonder what happened to Amelia Earhart.

A Birthday Party for Fish

by Ali Reich

"Jump into the water!
Buzz across the lake!
Come to my party!
Eat some birthday cake!"

"I'd be very happy
To buzz across the lake,
To help you make your birthday wish,
To eat your birthday cake."

"Jump INTO the water?
I'm in the water NOW.
We can play some birthday games.
I'll come and show you how!"

The Bear's Toothache by David McPhail

One night I <u>heard</u> something <u>under</u> my window.

It was a bear with a toothache.

I told him to come in, and I looked at his tooth.

I tried to pull it out.

It would not move.

"Maybe eating something will move it
a little," said the bear.

The bear ate some hamburgers and
everything else he could find.

The food was all gone, but the tooth
was the same as before.

When we got back to my room, I
tried to hit the tooth with my pillow.
But the bear ducked, and I hit the
lamp.
The lamp fell down.
Crash!

The crash <u>woke</u> my father.

He got up and came to my room.

"What happened to the <u>lamp</u>?" he asked.

"It fell down," I answered.

"Oh," he said.

And he went back to bed.

Then I had a good idea.

I put one end of a rope on the bear's
tooth and the other end on the bed.

Then the bear got on the window sill and
jumped.

And just as he hit the ground,
the tooth popped out!
The bear was so happy that he
gave me the tooth to
put <u>under</u> my pillow.

Herman by Mace Rosen

It was nearly the end of the day in Mrs. Young's room at Downs School.

Mrs. Young said, "Children, before you go home, read this."

This is what Mrs. Young wanted the children to read.

In two days we will talk about the things we like.
So come to school with something you like more than anything else.
It has to be something little enough to fit in a box or bag.
Be ready to talk about the thing you like.

After school that day everyone
started talking at once.

"I know what I'll do," said Jo Bridges.
"I'll come with my very own clock.
It makes the best buzzing noise you have
heard."

"Some of my little cars and airplanes
will fit in a box," said Peg Black.

Ned Parks said he was going to come
with a beautiful book that had big
pictures on every page.

Jack Ball thought he would take his
thick white sweater from Ireland to school.

Mark Lee could not think of a thing.
All the way home from school he wondered
and wondered.

"Everyone but me seems to have an idea,"
Mark thought.

Then an idea came to him.

"I know what to take!" he said.

"And will everyone be surprised!"

The big day came.

All the children in the room had the things they liked best with them.

Mrs. Young asked the girls and boys to put the things out where everyone could see them.

And everyone but Mark did.

Mark put his box under the window sill.

Then one by one the children talked about and showed the things they liked best.

All at once there was a big crash.
The little tree that the PTA gave the
room flew off the window sill.

"How could that have happened?" asked
Mrs. Young.
"It could not fly off by itself."

No one had time to wonder long.
All the children were hard at work
putting the little tree in a new pot.

As they worked, there were other noises.
One book fell. Then another.

"I am tired of this," said Mrs. Young.
"We have to find out what is happening."

The girls and boys looked and looked.

Jo said, "The thing that was moving
things is not here.
It's gone now."

Then Ned said, "Look, a snake!
What is it doing here?
Do you think it moved the
books and the tree?"

"Snake?" said Mark. "That's Herman.

He is the thing I like best.

He was in the grass near my house."

"Take your turn now, Mark," said Peg.
"We want to hear more about your snake."

So Mark picked up Herman and walked to
the front of the room.

"I wanted to surprise you," said Mark.
"But Herman surprised me, too!"

192